Joseph Haydn

Symphony No. 103 in E♭ major / Es-Dur

Hob. I:103 'Drum Roll'/„mit dem Paukenwirbel"

Edited by / Herausgegeben von
Harry Newstone

EULENBURG

EAS 158
ISBN 978-3-7957-6558-3
ISMN 979-0-2002-2546-4

Edition based on Eulenburg Study Score ETP 469

Ernst Eulenburg Ltd
48 Great Marlborough Street
London W1F 7BB

Contents / Inhalt

III. Menuet/Trio 54 Track 3

IV. Finale. Allegro con spirito 63 Track 4

Preface

Composed: 1795 in London
First performance: 2 March 1795 in London
Original publisher: André, Offenbach, 1799
Instrumentation: 2 Flutes, 2 Oboes, 2 Clarinets, 2 Bassoons – 2 Horns, 2 Trumpets – Timpani – Strings
Duration: ca. 28 minutes

In the autumn of 1790 Prince Nikolaus Joseph Esterházy, Haydn's employer and patron, died and his son, Prince Paul Anton, succeeded him. Almost at once the great (but considerably expensive) musical establishment which had for nearly thirty years nurtured the composer, and is now chiefly remembered for the glory he brought to it, was dismantled. Although still nominally Capellmeister, with a yearly pension, Haydn was at last free to travel wherever he wished, something he had not been able to do before. He returned to Vienna relieved of the daily pressures of court duties, but his respite was not to last long. Johann Peter Salomon, the German-born violinist and London impresario, was visiting Cologne when he heard of the death of Prince Nikolaus and lost no time in getting to Vienna determined to procure Haydn for his forthcoming London season. It was not the first time he had invited Haydn to England; now the composer was free to accept, and he did. A contract was exchanged and the two left Vienna in the middle of December and arrived in Dover on New Year's Day 1791.

Haydn stayed in England for a year and a half and returned for a second visit of similar duration in 1794-5. The stimulus he received from the London musical scene, the reception he was accorded there and the high quality of the musicians placed at his disposal inspired him to some of his finest music. The twelve symphonies he wrote for Salomon (six for each visit) are the summation of his orchestral achievement and the ground upon which the music he composed after his return to Vienna – notably the last six masses, *The Creation* and *The Seasons* – was based.

The most popular of the London symphonies are among the most frequently played of Haydn's works, yet for very many years they were (and often still are) performed from texts that had, during the 19th century, become seriously corrupted from the originals. The first modern attempt to present a uniform set of scores based upon authentic sources came with Ernst Praetorius's edition for Eulenberg in the 1930s. For this he consulted the autograph scores of Nos. 98, 99, 101, 102, 103 and 104 but not those of Nos. 94, 95, 96 and 100 (No. 93 has disappeared and the whereabouts of No.97 was then unknown). One can only speculate on why Praetorius was not able to examine the autograph of No. 94 which was in the then

Preußische Staatsbibliothek in Berlin, where he had seen those of Nos. 98, 99, 101, 102 and 104, or Nos. 95 and 96 which were in the British Museum along with No. 103 of which he had received a photocopy. Clearly, detailed knowledge of the whereabouts of Haydn autographs was still very sketchy in the 1930s and Praetorius probably had no way of knowing what we, with the benefit of a further 50 years of Haydn research, can take for granted. Thus Praetorius's edition, while the best available at the time and certainly an important step in the right direction was, not surprisingly, uneven.

The phase of Haydn research that was to result in no less than a renaissance was now well begun. In 1939 the distinguished Danish scholar Jens Peter Larsen published *Die Haydn-Überlieferung* and two years later a facsimile print of *Drei Haydn-Kataloge*, revealing for the first time the immensity of the subject. The post-war years saw the formation in London of the Haydn Orchestra and in Boston of the Haydn Society (both 1949). In 1954, the founder of the Haydn Society, H.C. Robbins Landon, in an article *The original versions of Haydn's first 'Salomon' symphonies*, drew our attention to the extent to which the standard performing editions of these works (mostly Breitkopf & Härtel and Peters) were in many cases 'flagrant falsifications of Haydn's own texts'. For a discussion on how these alterations came about the reader is referred to that article as well as to Landon's *The Symphonies of Joseph Haydn*, and his *Haydn – Chronicle and Works*, Vol. 3 *Haydn in England.*

Since the mid-1950s Henle Verlag, Munich, has issued a number of volumes of Haydn symphonies as part of a Complete Edition of his works for the Haydn Institute of Cologne. Universal Edition, Vienna, issued all the symphonies during the 1960s in an edition by H. C. Robbins Landon.

In 1959, the present writer, with material and advice from Professor Landon, revised and conducted all the London symphonies in a series of BBC broadcasts commemorating the 150th anniversary of the composer's death. The aim was to get as close as possible to Haydn's original intentions not only from the scholar's point of view but from the performer's too.

The texts were accordingly prepared from a number of manuscript sources of primary authenticity and one early printed edition of unusual interest and importance.

Symphony No. 103

The Symphony No. 103 was composed during Haydn's second visit to England (1794–95) and the autograph score has on its front page the date '795' and 'Sinfonia in Es'. It was first performed under the composer's direction at the King's Theatre, Haymarket, London on 2 March 1795 at the fourth concert of G. B. Viotti's Opera Concert series and repeated at the seventh concert on 27 April. It will be recalled that Haydn's last three symphonies, although originally commissioned by Johann Peter Salomon for his own London concerts, were first given at Viotti's concerts, Salomon having discontinued his series at the beginning of 1795 because the war with France had made it impossible for him to obtain artists from the continent of 'the first talents'. Haydn's move to Viotti's series was made entirely with Salomon's blessing and the composer and his former impresario/concertmaster remained on the most cordial of terms; indeed, Salomon appeared frequently as soloist in the Opera Concert series.

Viotti's orchestra numbered some 60 players including, no doubt, doubled woodwind (and possibly brass) as evidenced by the 'solo' and 'tutti' indications in the orchestral parts. The *Andante* was encored at the first performance and the leader, William Cramer, singled out for special praise for his solo playing.

The autograph score was given by Haydn to Luigi Cherubini (1760–1842) in 1806 with the charming dedication over the composer's signature, 'Padre del celebre Cherubini/ai 24tro de Febr. 806', when the latter visited him in Vienna. It was bought from Cherubini's grandson in 1879 by Julian Marshall from whom the British Museum acquired it not long thereafter.

An unsolved puzzle surrounds the Menuet, the first two pages of which in the autograph and the last page of the Trio are in a strange and somewhat unsteady hand. An annotation in the score by Julian Marshall suggests that the original pages were lost and were recopied by Cherubini, but H. C. Robbins Landon in his edition of the Symphony rejects that the handwriting is Cherubini's.[1] The paper is the same as the rest of the autograph in which there are a number of blank pages.

Harry Newstone

[1] *Joseph Haydn, the complete symphonies*, ed. H. C. Robbins Landon, Vol. XII, Vienna, 1968, LXXXI

Vorwort

komponiert: 1795 in London
Uraufführung: 2. März 1795 in London
Originalverlag: André, Offenbach, 1799
Orchesterbesetzung: 2 Flöten, 2 Oboen, 2 Klarinetten, 2 Fagotte – 2 Hörner, 2 Trompeten – Pauken – Streicher
Spieldauer: etwa 28 Minuten

Im Herbst 1790 starb Fürst Nikolaus Joseph Esterházy, Haydns Dienstherr und Gönner; Fürst Paul Anton, sein Sohn, folgte ihm nach. Fast unmittelbar hierauf wurde das bedeutende, allerdings ziemlich kostspielige Musikleben am Hofe eingestellt, das Haydn nahezu dreißig Jahre lang ernährt hatte und an das man sich heute hauptsächlich des Glanzes wegen erinnert, den es durch den Komponisten erhalten hatte. Obwohl er auch weiterhin den Kapellmeistertitel führen durfte und eine jährliche Pension erhielt, konnte Haydn im Gegensatz zu früher nun schließlich nach Belieben reisen. Er kehrte nach Wien zurück, entlastet vom täglichen Zwang des Dienstes am Hofe, jedoch sollte diese Ruhepause nicht von langer Dauer sein. Als der deutschstämmige Geiger und Londoner Impresario Johann Peter Salomon während eines Aufenthaltes in Köln vom Tod des Fürsten Nikolaus erfuhr, eilte er unverzüglich nach Wien, entschlossen, Haydn für die kommende Saison nach London zu verpflichten. Dies war nicht das erste Mal, dass er Haydn nach England eingeladen hatte; jetzt jedoch war der Komponist in der Lage zuzusagen, und er tat es auch. Ein Vertrag wurde ausgehandelt und die beiden verließen Wien Mitte Dezember und erreichten Dover am Neujahrstag 1791.

Haydn blieb anderthalb Jahre lang in England und kehrte 1794/95 zu einem zweiten, etwa gleich langen Aufenthalt zurück. Die Anregungen, die er durch das Londoner Musikleben erhielt, die Aufnahme dort und die hohe Qualität der ihm zur Verfügung stehenden Musiker inspirierten ihn zu mehreren seiner bedeutendsten Werke. So bilden die zwölf Sinfonien für Salomon (sechs für jeden Aufenthalt) die Zusammenfassung seiner ganzen Kunst der Orchesterkomposition und die Grundlage für die Werke, die er nach seiner Rückkehr nach Wien schrieb – vor allem die sechs letzten Messen sowie die *Schöpfung* und die *Jahreszeiten*.

Die bekanntesten der Londoner Sinfonien gehören zu den meistgespielten Werken Haydns, jedoch wurden sie viele Jahre lang (vielfach noch bis in die heutige Zeit) aus Notenmaterial aufgeführt, das im 19. Jahrhundert gegenüber dem Originaltext erheblich verfälscht worden war. Den ersten neueren Versuch, aufgrund der authentischen Quellen einen einheitlichen Satz Partituren herauszubringen, stellt die Ausgabe von Ernst Praetorius im Rahmen der

Edition Eulenberg in den 1930er Jahren dar. Er zog die Partitur-Autographe von Nr. 98, 99, 101, 102, 103 und 104 heran. Nicht aber diejenigen von Nr. 94, 95, 96 und 100 (das Autograph von Nr. 93 ist verschollen, und das von Nr. 97 war damals nicht nachweisbar). Man kann nur Vermutungen darüber anstellen, warum Praetorius nicht in der Lage war, das Autograph von Nr. 94 zu untersuchen, das in der damaligen Preußischen Staatsbibliothek in Berlin lag, wo er auch die Autographe von Nr. 98, 99, 101, 102 und 104 eingesehen hatte; Nr. 95 und 96 waren ihm im British Museum London zugänglich, zusammen mit dem Autograph von Nr. 103, das ihm als Fotokopie vorlag. Auf jeden Fall war die Kenntnis der Aufbewahrungsorte von Haydn-Autographen in den 1930er Jahren noch sehr lückenhaft und Praetorius konnte damals wohl kaum wissen, was wir heute, nach weiteren 50 Jahren Haydn-Forschung, als erwiesen betrachten können. So war es nicht verwunderlich, dass die Ausgaben von Praetorius in sich uneinheitlich waren, auch wenn sie zu ihrer Zeit die besten verfügbaren waren und sicherlich einen Schritt in die richtige Richtung unternahmen.

Damit hatte eine Zeit intensiver Haydn-Forschung begonnen, die eine regelrechte Renaissance auslöste. 1939 veröffentlichte der bedeutende dänische Musikwissenschaftler Jens Peter Larsen sein Buch *Die Haydn-Überlieferung* und zwei Jahre später als Faksimile *Drei Haydn-Kataloge*; damit wies er erstmals auf die nahezu unüberschaubaren Dimensionen dieses Forschungsbereichs hin. In den Nachkriegsjahren folgten die Gründung des Haydn-Orchesters London und in Bosten die der Haydn-Gesellschaft (beide 1949), 1954 machte H. C. Robbins Landon, Begründer der Haydn-Gesellschaft, in einem Aufsatz *The original versions of Haydn's first 'Salomon' symphonies* auf das Ausmaß aufmerksam, in dem das verfügbare Aufführungsmaterial dieser Werke (hauptsächlich von Breitkopf & Härtel und Peters) in vielen Fällen durch „offenkundige Verfälschung von Haydn's eigenem Notentext" entstellt war. Bezüglich einer eingehenden Darstellung, wie es zu diesen Abweichungen kam, sei hier auf den Aufsatz sowie auf Landons Arbeiten *The Symphonies of Joseph Haydn* und *Haydn – Chronicle and Works* (Bd. 3 *Haydn in England*) hingewiesen.

Seit Mitte der 1950er Jahre hat der Henle-Verlag München im Rahmen einer Gesamtausgabe der Werke Haydns durch das Haydn-Institut Köln mehrere Bände mit Sinfonien veröffentlicht. Bei der Universal Edition Wien erschienen alle Sinfonien in den 1960er Jahren in einer Ausgabe von H. C. Robbins Landon.

1959 revidierte der Herausgeber der hier vorliegenden Ausgabe anlässlich einer Sendereihe der BBC zum 150. Todestage des Komponisten, in der er selbst alle Londoner Sinfonien Haydns dirigierte, die Partituren, wofür ihm Robbins Landon eigenes Material und seinen Rat zur Verfügung stellte. Das Ziel war, Haydns eigenen Intentionen nicht nur vom wissenschaftlichen Standpunkt aus, sondern auch aus der Sicht des ausübenden Musikers so nahe wie möglich zu kommen.

Der Notentext wurde aufgrund einer Anzahl handschriftlicher Primärquellen und einer besonders interessanten und wichtigen Druckausgabe erarbeitet.

Sinfonie Nr. 103

Haydn komponierte die Sinfonie Nr. 103 während seines zweiten England-Besuchs 1794/95. Auf dem Titelblatt der autographen Partitur stehen das Datum „795" und „Sinfonia in Es". Die Erstaufführung fand unter der Leitung des Komponisten am 2. März 1795 beim fünften Konzert von Viottis „Opera Concerts" im Londoner King's Theatre am Haymarket statt; eine Wiederholung folgte im siebten Konzert am 27. April. Wie allseits bekannt, gab ursprünglich Salomon Haydns letzte Sinfonien für seine eigenen Londoner Konzerte in Auftrag, doch wurden sie in Viottis Konzerten vorgestellt, nachdem Salomon seine Konzertreihe Anfang 1795 eingestellt hatte: Der Krieg mit Frankreich hatte es ihm unmöglich gemacht, vom europäischen Festland Künstler „allererster Güte" zu bekommen. Haydns Wechsel zu den Konzerten Viottis fand durchaus mit Salomons Billigung statt; der Komponist und sein vorheriger Impresario-Konzertmeister blieben auf überaus freundlichem Fuß. Salomon trat sogar häufig in den Opera Concerts als Solist auf.

Viottis Orchester zählte etwa 60 Spieler, darunter ohne Zweifel doppelt besetzte Holzbläser (und möglicherweise Blechbläser), wie aus den „solo"- und „tutti"-Eintragungen in den Orchesterstimmen hervorgeht. Das Andante wurde bei der Uraufführung wiederholt; der Konzertmeister, William Cramer, wurde wegen seines Solospiels besonders hervorgehoben.

Im Jahre 1806 überreichte Haydn die autographe Partitur an Luigi Cherubini (1760–1842), der ihn in Wien besuchte, mit einer reizenden Widmung über der Signierung des Komponisten: „Padre del celebre Cherubini/ai 24tro de Febr. 806." Julian Marshall erwarb es 1879 von Cherubinis Enkel, nicht lange darauf ging es in den Besitz des British Museum über.

Ein nicht gelöstes Rätsel gibt das Menuet auf, dessen erste zwei Seiten des Autographs und die letzte Seite des Trios von einer unbekannten und ein wenig unsicheren Hand stammen. Eine Anmerkung Julian Marshalls in der Partitur lässt vermuten, dass die Originalseiten verlorengegangen waren und von Cherubini noch einmal abgeschrieben wurden. H. C. Robbins Landon bestreitet in seiner Ausgabe der Sinfonie jedoch, dass es sich um Cherubinis Handschrift handele.[1] Das Papier ist dasselbe wie beim übrigen Autograph, worin einige Seiten unbeschrieben sind.

Harry Newstone

[1] *Joseph Haydn, the complete symphonies*, hg. von H. C. Robbins Landon, Bd. XII, Wien, 1968, S. LXXXI

Symphony No. 103
'Drum Roll'

Joseph Haydn
(1732–1809)
Hob. I:103

In Nomine Domini

Edited by Harry Newstone

9
Fl. 1 2
[a 2]
p
Ob. 1 2
p
1.
Fg. 1 2
Cor. (E♭) 1 2
p
I
Vl.
II
p
p
Vc.
Cb.
17
Ob. 1 2
p
Fg. 1 2
p
Cor. (E♭) 1 2
p
I
Vl.
II
Vla.
p
Vc.
e Cb.

23
[a 2]
Fl. 1 2
p
Ob. 1 2
[p]
Fg. 1 2
p
Cor. (E♭) 1 2
[p]
I
Vl.
II
Vla.
Vc.
Cb.
31
Ob. 1 2
Fg. 1 2
a 2
fz
fz
fz
pp
I
Vl.
II
Vla.
Vc.
Cb.
fz p fz p fz pp

Allegro con spirito
40
Fl.
Ob.
Cl. (B♭)
Fg.
Cor. (E♭)
Tr. (E♭)
Timp.
Vl.
I
II
Vla.
Vc.
Cb.

44
Fl. 1 2
[a 2]
Ob. 1 2
a 2
Cl. (B♭) 1 2
a 2
Fg. 1 2
a 2
Cor. (E♭) 1 2
Tr. (E♭) 1 2
Timp.
I
Vl.
II
Vla.
Vc.
Cb.

48
[a 2]
Fl. 1 2
a 2
Ob. 1 2
a 2
Cl. (B♭) 1 2
a 2
Fg. 1 2
Cor. (E♭) 1 2
a 2
Tr. (E♭) 1 2
a 2
Timp.
I
Vl.
II
Vla.
Vc.
Cb.

52
[a 2]
Fl. 1 2
fz
fz
Ob. 1 2
fz
fz
Cl. (B♭) 1 2
fz
fz
a 2
Fg. 1 2
fz
fz
a 2
Cor. (E♭) 1 2
fz
fz
a 2
Tr. (E♭) 1 2
fz
fz
Timp.
fz
fz
I
Vl.
fz
fz
II
fz
fz
Vla.
fz
fz
Vc. e Cb.
fz
fz

57
[a 2]
Fl. 1 2
Soli
1.
Ob. 1 2
a 2
Cl. (B♭) 1 2
a 2
Fg. 1 2
Cor. (E♭) 1 2
Tr. (E♭) 1 2
Timp.
I
Vl.
II
Vla.
Vc. e Cb.

62
[a 2]
Fl. 1 2
f
fz
1.
Ob. 1 2
[f]
a 2
Cl. (B♭) 1 2
a 2
Fg. 1 2
Cor. (E♭) 1 2
a 2
Tr. (E♭) 1 2
Timp.
I
Vl.
II
Vla.
Vc. e Cb.

67
[a 2]
Fl. 1 2
fz
ff
Ob. 1 2
Cl. (B♭) 1 2
a 2
Fg. 1 2
Cor. (E♭) 1 2
a 2
Tr. (E♭) 1 2
Timp.
I
Vl.
II
Vla.
Vc. e Cb.

72
[a 2]
Fl. 1 2
Ob. 1 2
Cl. (B♭) 1 2
a 2
Fg. 1 2
fz
Cor. (E♭) 1 2
Tr. (E♭) 1 2
Timp.
I
Vl.
II
fz
fz
[·]
Vla.
fz
Vc. e Cb.
fz

[a 2]
77
Fl. 1 2
1. Solo
Ob. 1 2
p
Cl. (B♭) 1 2
a 2
Fg. 1 2
Cor. (E♭) 1 2
Tr. (E♭) 1 2
Timp.
I
Vl.
II
p
p
Vla.
p
pizz.
Vc. e Cb.
[p]

83
Fl. 1 2
[a 2]
Ob. 1 2
1.
Cl. (B♭) 1 2
Fg. 1 2
a 2
Cor. (E♭) 1 2
a 2
Tr. (E♭) 1 2
a 2
Timp.
I
Vl.
II
Vla.
Vc. e Cb.
arco

[a 2]
88
Fl. 1 2
Ob. 1 2
Cl. (B♭) 1 2
a 2
Fg. 1 2
a 2
Cor. (E♭) 1 2
a 2
Tr. (E♭) 1 2
Timp.
I
Vl.
II
Vla.
Vc. e Cb.

94
[Solo]
Fg. 1 2
p
I
Vl.
II
p
p
Vla.
p
Vc.
Vc. e Cb.
p
99
[a 2]
Fl. 1 2
p
I
Vl.
II
Vla.
Vc.

105
[a 2]
Fl. 1 2
cresc.
f
1.
Ob. 1 2
p
cresc.
f
Cl. (B♭) 1 2
f
a 2
Fg. 1 2
f
Cor. (E♭) 1 2
f
Tr. (E♭) 1 2
f
Timp.
f
I
Vl.
II
cresc.
f
cresc.
f
Vla.
cresc.
f
Vc.
cresc.
f
Cb.
f

109
[a 2]
Fl. 1 2
Ob. 1 2
Cl. (B♭) 1 2
a 2
Fg. 1 2
a 2
Cor. (E♭) 1 2
a 2
Tr. (E♭) 1 2
Timp.
I
Vl.
II
Vla.
Vc.
Vc. e Cb.

115
Vl.
I
II
Vla.
Vc.
121
Fl.
Ob.
Cl. (B♭)
Fg.
Cor. (E♭)
[a 2]
a 2
p
f
cresc.
Vc.
Vc.
e Cb.
Tutti

[a 2]
126
Fl. 1 2
Ob. 1 2
a 2
Cl. (B♭) 1 2
a 2
Fg. 1 2
p
a 2
Cor. (E♭) 1 2
I
Vl.
II
p
p
Vla.
p
Vc. e Cb.
p
131
[Solo]
Fl. 1 2
p
[Soli]
Ob. 1 2
p
Solo
Fg. 1 2
[p]
I
Vl.
p
II
p
Vla.
p
Vc.
p
Cb.
p

[1.]
136
Fl. 1 2
Ob. 1 2
Cl. (B♭) 1 2
[Soli]
Cor. (E♭) 1 2
Soli
[p]
I
Vl.
II
Vla.
Vc.
142 [1.]
Fl. 1 2
Ob. 1 2
p
Cl. (B♭) 1 2
Fg. 1 2
p
I
Vl.
II
Vla.
pizz.
Vc. e Cb.

146
Fl. 1 2
Ob. 1 2
Cl. (B♭) 1 2
Fg. 1 2
Vl. I II
Vla.
Vc. e Cb.
[1.]
[a 2]
[p]
[Tutti]
[Tutti]
a 2
f
arco
150
[a 2]
a 2
p
fz
ff
Cor. (E♭) 1 2
Tr. (E♭) 1 2
Timp.
[Tutti]
[f]

[a 2]
154
Fl. 1 2
Ob. 1 2
Cl. (B♭) 1 2
a 2
Fg. 1 2
Cor. (E♭) 1 2
Tr. (E♭) 1 2
Timp.
I
Vl.
II
Vla.
Vc. e Cb.
p
159
[♭]
[·]

164
[a 2]
Fl. 1 2
a 2
Ob. 1 2
a 2
Cl. (B♭) 1 2
a 2
Fg. 1 2
Cor. (E♭) 1 2
Tr. (E♭) 1 2
Timp.
I
Vl.
II
Vla.
Vc.
Cb.

168 [a 2]
Fl. 1 2
a 2
Ob. 1 2
a 2
Cl. (B♭) 1 2
a 2
Fg. 1 2
Cor. (E♭) 1 2
a 2
Tr. (E♭) 1 2
a 2
Timp.
I
Vl.
II
Vla.
Vc.
Cb.

172 [a 2]
Fl. 1 2
fz
Ob. 1 2
Cl. (B♭) 1 2
a 2
Fg. 1 2
a 2
Cor. (E♭) 1 2
a 2
Tr. (E♭) 1 2
Timp.
I
Vl.
II
Vla.
Vc. e Cb.

177 [a 2]
Fl. 1 2
Ob. 1 2
1. Solo
p
Cl. (B♭) 1 2
a 2
Fg. 1 2
Soli
Cor. (E♭) 1 2
p
Tr. (E♭) 1 2
Timp.
I
Vl.
II
p
p
Vla.
p
pizz.
Vc. e Cb.
[p]

182
Fl. 1 2
[a 2]
f
1.
Ob. 1 2
[Tutti]
Cl. (B♭) 1 2
a 2
Fg. 1 2
Cor. (E♭) 1 2
Tr. (E♭) 1 2
Timp.
I
Vl.
II
Vla.
arco
Vc. e Cb.

187 [a 2]
Fl. 1 2
fz
Ob. 1 2
fz
a 2
Cl. (B♭) 1 2
f[z]
a 2
Fg. 1 2
fz
a 2
Cor. (E♭) 1 2
ff
a 2
Tr. (E♭) 1 2
ff
Timp.
ff
I
Vl.
II
ff
Vla.
ff
Vc. e Cb.
ff

[a 2]
191
Fl. 1 2
fz
f
Ob. 1 2
fz
f
Cl. (B♭) 1 2
f [z]
f
a 2
Fg. 1 2
fz
f
a 2
Cor. (E♭) 1 2
ff
f
a 2
Tr. (E♭) 1 2
ff
f
Timp.
ff
f
I
Vl.
II
ff
fz
fz
[f]
fz
fz
ff
f
Vla.
ff
f
Vc. e Cb.
ff
f
195 [a 2]
Fl. 1 2
Ob. 1 2
1. Solo
Cl. (B♭) 1 2
[p]
a 2
Fg. 1 2
Cor. (E♭) 1 2
I
Vl.
II
fz
fz
fz
fz
p
p
Vla.
p
Vc.
Vc. e Cb.
p

Adagio
201
[a 2]
Fl. 1 2
Ob. 1 2
Cl. (B♭) 1 2
Solo
Fg. 1 2
p [e sostenuto]
Cor. (E♭) 1 2
Intrada
Solo
Timp.
[f]
I
Vl.
II
Vla.
p [e sostenuto]
Vc.
p [e sostenuto]
Cb.
p [e sostenuto]

Tempo I [Allegro con spirito]
213
[a 2]
Fl. 1 2
f
f
Ob. 1 2
a 2
f
f
Cl. (B♭) 1 2
a 2
f
f
Fg. 1 2
1.
a 2
f
f
Cor. (E♭) 1 2
a 2
f
f
Tr. (E♭) 1 2
f
f
Timp.
f
f
I
Vl.
II
f
fz
Vla.
f
fz
Vc. e Cb.
f
fz

218 [a 2]
Fl. 1 2
Ob. 1 2
Soli
[Tutti]
Cl. (B♭) 1 2
Soli
[Tutti]
Fg. 1 2
a 2
[Soli]
a 2
Cor. (E♭) 1 2
Soli
[Tutti]
Tr. (E♭) 1 2
Timp.
I
Vl.
II
Vla.
Vc. e Cb.

Finis Laus Deo

II. Andante più tosto Allegretto

15
I
Vl.
II
Vla.
Vc.
e Cb.
21
I
Vl.
II
Vla.
Vc.
e Cb.
27
Ob. 1 2
Fg. 1 2
a 2
Cor. (C) 1 2
I
Vl.
II
Vla.
Vc.
e Cb.
p
fz
tr
[fz]

35
1.
Ob. 1 2
Fg. 1 2
a 2
Cor. (C) 1 2
I
Vl.
II
Vla.
Vc. e Cb.
tr
fz
p
pp
40
1.
Ob. 1 2
Cor. (C) 1 2
I
Vl.
II
Vla.
Vc. e Cb.
fz

44
Ob. 1 2
Fg. 1 2
a 2
Cor. (C) 1 2
I
Vl.
II
Vla.
Vc. e Cb.
tr
fz
p
pp
51
[Solo]
Ob. 1 2
I
Vl.
II
Vla.
Vc. e Cb.

57
Solo
Fl. 1 2
Ob. 1 2
Fg. 1 2
I
Vl.
II
Vla.
Vc. e Cb.
64
a 2

70
1.
Fl. 1 2
Ob. 1 2
1.
Fg. 1 2
Solo
I
Vl.
II
Vla.
75
Ob. 1 2
1.
Fg. 1 2
1.
I
Vl.
II
Vla.
Vc.
tr
tr

80
Fl. 1 2
Ob. 1 2
Fg. 1 2
Vl. I
Vl. II
Vla.
Vc. e Cb.
85
Solo Vl. I
Rip.
Vl. II
Vla.
Vc. e Cb.
89
Solo Vl. I
Rip.
Vl. II
Vla.
Vc. e Cb.

93
Fg. 1 2
Cor. (C) 1 2
Solo
Vl. I
Rip.
[arco]
[arco]
Vl. II
Vla.
[arco]
Vc. e Cb.
96
Fg. 1 2
Cor. (C) 1 2
Solo
Vl. I
Rip.
Vl. II
Vla.
Vc. e Cb.

100
Cor. (C) 1 2
Solo
Vl. I
Rip.
Vl. II
Vla.
Vc. e Cb.
105
Cor. (C) 1 2
Solo
Vl. I
Rip.
Vl. II
Vla.
Vc. e Cb.
p
pizz.
pizz.
pizz.

109
Tutti
Fl. 1 2
a 2
Ob. 1 2
Fg. 1 2
Cor. (C) 1 2
Tr. (C) 1 2
Timp.
Tutti
[arco]
I
Vl.
II
Vla.
arco
Vc.
e Cb.
114
Vc.
Tutti

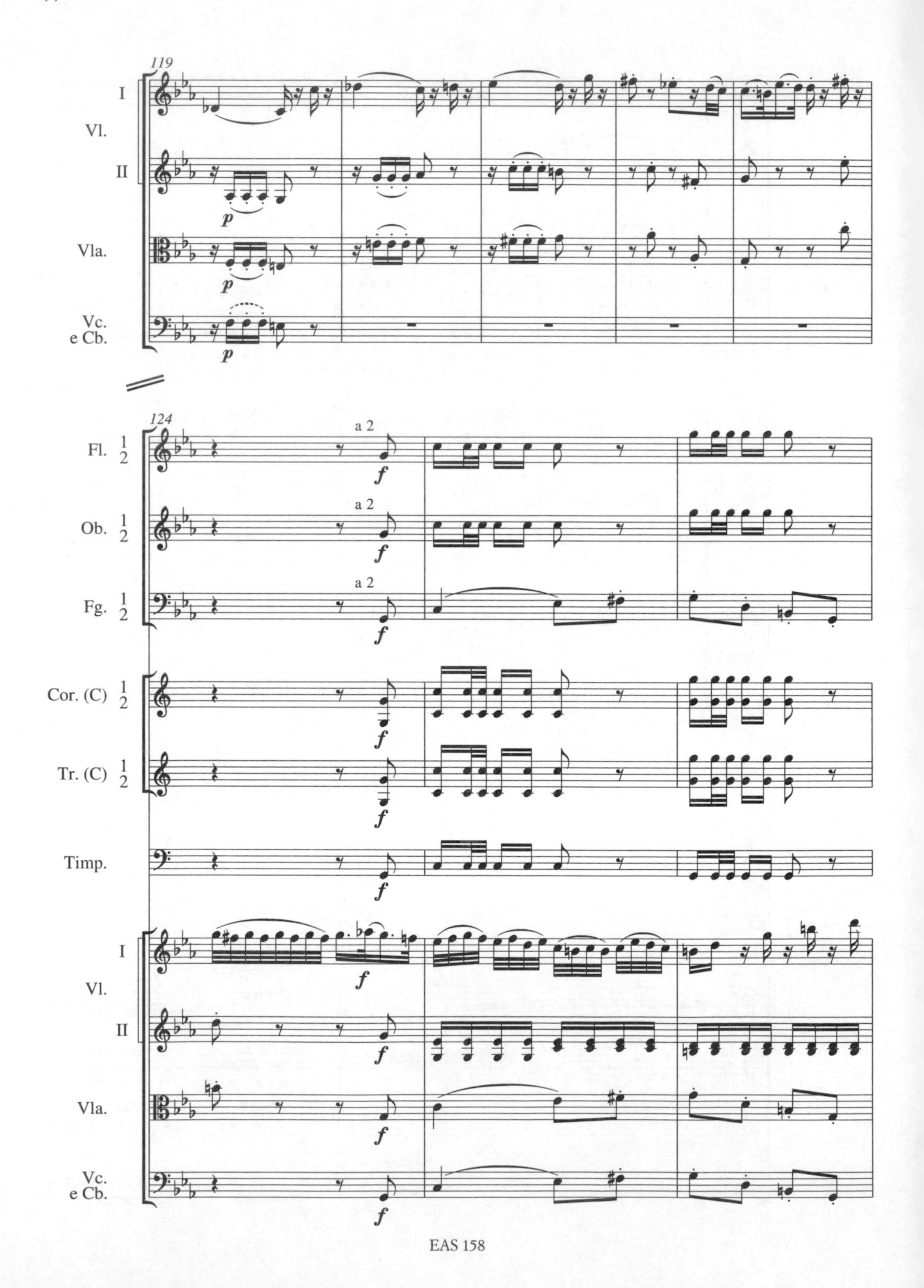
119
I
Vl.
II
Vla.
Vc.
e Cb.
124
a 2
Fl. 1 2
Ob. 1 2
Fg. 1 2
Cor. (C) 1 2
Tr. (C) 1 2
Timp.
I
Vl.
II
Vla.
Vc.
e Cb.

127
a 2
Fl. 1 2
a 2
Ob. 1 2
a 2
Fg. 1 2
Cor. (C) 1 2
Tr. (C) 1 2
Timp.
I
Vl.
II
Vla.
Vc.
e Cb.
131
a 2
[Soli]
a 2

135
Fl. 1 2
Solo
Ob. 1 2
[Solo]
Fg. 1 2
Cor. (C) 1 2
pizz.
I
Vl.
II
Vla.
Vc. e Cb.
139
1.
[Tutti]
arco

143
Tutti
Fl. 1 2
Ob. 1 2
[a 2]
Fg. 1 2
[f]
Cor. (C) 1 2
Tr. (C) 1 2
Timp.
arco
I
Vl.
II
Vla.
arco
Vc.
arco
Cb.
148 a 2
Fl. 1 2
Ob. 1 2
a 2
Fg. 1 2
I
Vl.
II
Vla.
Vc. e Cb.

151
a 2
Fl. 1 2
Ob. 1 2
Fg. 1 2
Cor. (C) 1 2
Tr. (C) 1 2
Timp.
Vl. I II
Vla.
Vc. e Cb.
154

158
Fl. 1 2
Ob. 1 2
1.
Fg. 1 2
Cor. (C) 1 2
Tr. (C) 1 2
Timp.
I
Vl.
II
Vla.
Vc.
Cb.
p
fz
165
pp

[a 2]
172
Fl. 1 2
p
f
ff
1.
Ob. 1 2
a 2
Fg. 1 2
Cor. (C) 1 2
a 2
Tr. (C) 1 2
Timp.
[tr]
I
Vl.
II
pp
Vla.
Vc. e Cb.
178
Solo
[Solo]
[Solo]
Vl. I

1.
185
Fl. 1 2
Tutti
Ob. 1 2
[Tutti]
Fg. 1 2
Cor. (C) 1 2
Tr. (C) 1 2
Timp.
[tr]
Vl. I
II
Vla.
Vc. e Cb.

189
a 2
Fl. 1 2
Ob. 1 2
Fg. 1 2
Cor. (C) 1 2
Tr. (C) 1 2
Timp.
Vl. I II
Vla.
Vc. e Cb.
tr
fz

192
a 2
Fl. 1 2
p
[a 2]
ff
Ob. 1 2
a 2
Fg. 1 2
Cor. (C) 1 2
Tr. (C) 1 2
Timp.
I
Vl.
II
f
Vla.
Vc.
[fz]
Cb.

III. Menuet

[a 2]
Flauto 1 2
Oboe 1 2
Clarinetto (B♭) 1 2
[a 2]
Fagotto 1 2
Corno (E♭) 1 2
[f]
Tromba (E♭) 1
(Clarino) 2
Timpani
(E♭, B♭)
I
Violino
II
Viola
Violoncello
e Contrabasso

6
[a 2]
Fl. 1 2
Ob. 1 2
a 2
Cl. (B♭) 1 2
2.
1.
[a 2]
Fg. 1 2
Cor. (E♭) 1 2
a 2
Tr. (E♭) 1 2
Timp.
legato
I
Vl.
II
Vla.
Vc. e Cb.
13
[a 2]
1. Solo
Solo
[a 2]
1.
Cl. (B♭) 1 2
Cor. (E♭) 1 2

20
[a 2]
Fl. 1 2
fz
Ob. 1 2
Cl. (B♭) 1 2
a 2
[f]
Fg. 1 2
[a 2]
Cor. (E♭) 1 2
[f]
Tr. (E♭) 1 2
f
Timp.
[f]
Vl. I
Vl. II
Vla.
Vc. e Cb.

25
[a 2]
Fl. 1 2
fz
Ob. 1 2
fz
a 2
Cl. (B♭) 1 2
fz
[a 2]
Fg. 1 2
fz
Cor. (E♭) 1 2
fz
Tr. (E♭) 1 2
fz
Timp.
I
Vl.
II
fz
pp
fz
Vla.
fz
Vc. e Cb.
fz

31
[a 2]
Fl. 1 2
Ob. 1 2
Cl. (B♭) 1 2
[a 2]
Fg. 1 2
Cor. (E♭) 1 2
Tr. (E♭) 1 2
Timp.
I
Vl.
II
Vla.
Vc. e Cb.

37
[a 2]
Fl. 1 2
p
Ob. 1 2
p
Cl. (B♭) 1 2
p
[a 2]
Fg. 1 2
p
a 2
Cor. (E♭) 1 2
a 2
Tr. (E♭) 1 2
Timp.
I
Vl.
II
p
p
Vla.
p
Vc. e Cb.
p

Fl.
Ob.
Cl. (B♭)
Fg.
Cor. (E♭)
Tr. (E♭)
Timp.
Vl.
Vla.
Vc.
e Cb.
Trio
Solo
[Solo]
Cb.
pizz.

55
Cl. (B♭) 1
2
Fg. 1 2
[p]
Cor. (E♭) 1 2
p
Vl. I
II
Vla.
Vc.
Cb.
61
Cl. (B♭) 2
pizz.

Menuet da capo

IV. Finale

Allegro con spirito
Flauto 1 2
Oboe 1 2
Clarinetto (B♭) 1 2
Fagotto 1 2
Soli
Corno (E♭) 1 2
[f]
p
Tromba (E♭) 1 2
(Clarino)
Timpani
(E♭, B♭)
Violino I II
p
Viola
Violoncello
e Contrabasso
8
Cl. (B♭) 1 2
p
Cor. (E♭) 1 2
Vl. I II
p
p
Vla.
p
Vc.
e Cb.
p

15
1. Solo
Ob. 1 2
p
I
Vl.
II
Vla.
Vc. e Cb.
21
1.
cresc.
f
27
1.
Vc.
Cb.

34
Fg. 1 2
Solo
[p]
Vl. I II
Vla.
Vc.
Cb.
40
1.
Fg. 1 2
Cor. (E♭) 1 2
Soli
p
Vl. I II
Vla.
47
Cl. (B♭) 1 2
p
Cor. (E♭) 1 2
Vl. I II
Vla.
Vc. e Cb.

54
Ob. 1 2
p
I
Vl.
II
Vla.
Vc. e Cb.
60
Ob. 1 2
I
Vl.
II
Vla.
Vc. e Cb.
66
I
Vl.
II
Vla.
Vc. e Cb.

73
[a 2]
Fl. 1 2
Ob. 1 2
Cl. (B♭) 1 2
Tutti
Fg. 1 2
a 2
Cor. (E♭) 1 2
Tr. (E♭) 1 2
Timp.
I
Vl.
II
Vla.
Vc.
Cb.

80 [a 2]
Fl. 1 2
Ob. 1 2
Cl. (B♭) 1 2
Fg. 1 2
Cor. (E♭) 1 2
Tr. (E♭) 1 2
Vl. I II
Vla.
Vc. e Cb.
a 2
85 [a 2]
fz

91
[a 2]
Fl. 1 2
Ob. 1 2
Cl. (B♭) 1 2
Fg. 1 2
Cor. (E♭) 1 2
Tr. (E♭) 1 2
Timp.
I
Vl.
II
Vla.
Vc. e Cb.

96
[a 2]
Fl. 1 2
Ob. 1 2
Cl. (B♭) 1 2
Fg. 1 2
Cor. (E♭) 1 2
Tr. (E♭) 1 2
Timp.
I
Vl.
II
Vla.
Vc. e Cb.

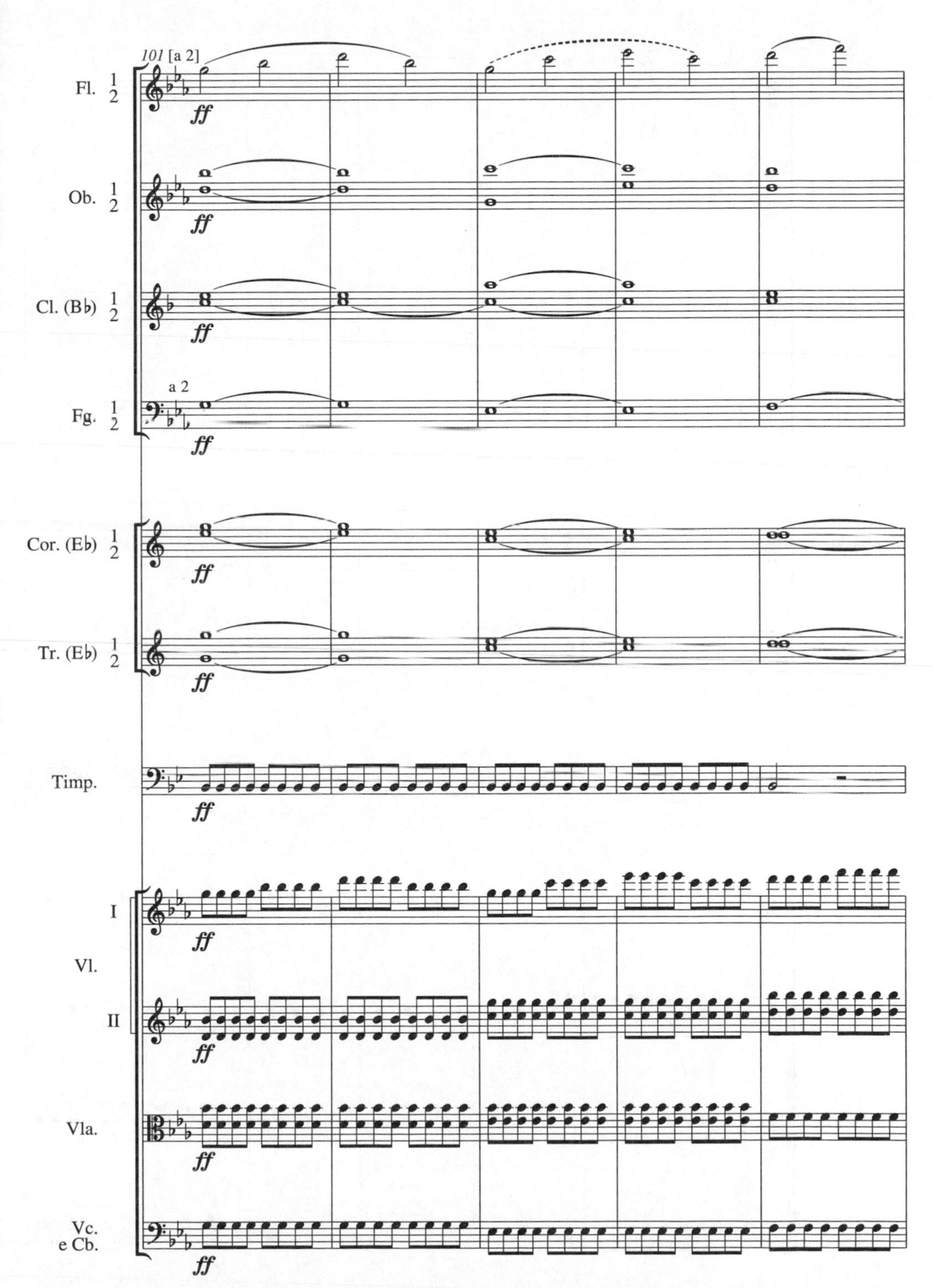
101 [a 2]
Fl. 1 2
ff
Ob. 1 2
ff
Cl. (B♭) 1 2
ff
a 2
Fg. 1 2
ff
Cor. (E♭) 1 2
ff
Tr. (E♭) 1 2
ff
Timp.
ff
I
Vl.
II
ff
ff
Vla.
ff
Vc. e Cb.
ff

106 [a 2]
Fl. 1 2
Ob. 1 2
Cl. (B♭) 1 2
a 2
Fg. 1 2
Cor. (E♭) 1 2
Tr. (E♭) 1 2
Timp.
I
Vl.
II
Vla.
Vc. e Cb.
p
p
p
p

112
Solo
Fl. 1 2
[p]
1. Solo
Ob. 1 2
p
I
Vl.
II
Vla.
Vc. e Cb.
118
I
Vl.
II
Vla.
Vc. e Cb.
125
Solo
Fg. 1 2
[p]
I
Vl.
II
Vla.
Vc. e Cb.

132
[a 2]
Fl. 1 2
[Tutti]
Ob. 1 2
Cl. (B♭) 1 2
Tutti
Fg. 1 2
Cor. (E♭) 1 2
Tr. (E♭) 1 2
Timp.
I
Vl.
II
Vla.
Vc. e Cb.

138 [a 2]
Fl. 1 2
Ob. 1 2
Cl. (B♭) 1 2
a 2
a 2
Fg. 1 2
a 2
Cor. (E♭) 1 2
a 2
Tr. (E♭) 1 2
Timp.
I
Vl.
II
Vla.
Vc.
e Cb.

144
[a 2]
Fl. 1 2
Ob. 1 2
Cl. (B♭) 1 2
a 2
Fg. 1 2
Cor. (E♭) 1 2
Tr. (E♭) 1 2
Timp.
I
Vl.
II
Vla.
Vc.
Vc. e Cb.
p

151
[a 2]
Fl. 1 2
Ob. 1 2
Cl. (B♭) 1 2
Fg. 1 2
Cor. (E♭) 1 2
Tr. (E♭) 1 2
Timp.
I
Vl.
II
Vla.
Vc.
Tutti
Vc. e Cb.
[cresc.]
cresc.
158
Cl. (B♭) 1 2
Soli
Cor. (E♭) 1 2
I
Vl.
II

165
Cl. (B♭) 1 2
I
Vl.
II
Vla.
p
Vc. e Cb.
p
171
1. [Solo]
Ob. 1 2
p
[cresc.]
[f]
1. Solo
Cl. (B♭) 1 2
I
Vl.
II
Vla.
Vc. e Cb.

178
Fl. 1 2
[a 2]
f
Ob. 1 2
1.
Cl. (B♭) 1 2
[Tutti]
f
Fg. 1 2
a 2
f
Cor. (E♭) 1 2
f
Tr. (E♭) 1 2
f
I
Vl.
II
f
Vla.
Vc. e Cb.
f

184 [a 2]
Fl. 1 2
Ob. 1 2
Cl. (B♭) 1 2
a 2
Fg. 1 2
a 2
f
Cor. (E♭) 1 2
Tr. (E♭) 1 2
Timp.
f
I
Vl.
II
Vla.
f
Vc. e Cb.
f

191
[a 2]
Fl. 1 2
Ob. 1 2
a 2
Cl. (B♭) 1 2
a 2
Fg. 1 2
Cor. (E♭) 1 2
Tr. (E♭) 1 2
Timp.
I
Vl.
II
p
Vla.
Vc. e Cb.

198 [a 2]
Fl. 1 2
a 2
Cl. (B♭) 1 2
I
Vl.
II
p
Vla.
p
Vc. e Cb.
p
205
[a 2]
Fl. 1 2
f
fz
fz
Ob. 1 2
f
fz
fz
Cl. (B♭) 1 2
f
fz
fz
a 2
Fg. 1 2
f
fz
fz
I
Vl.
II
Vla.
Vc. e Cb.

211
[a 2]
Fl. 1 2
fz
fz
fz
ff
Ob. 1 2
Cl. (B♭) 1 2
a 2
Fg. 1 2
Cor. (E♭) 1 2
a 2
f
Tr. (E♭) 1 2
Timp.
I
Vl.
II
Vla.
Vc. e Cb.

216 [a 2]
Fl. 1 2
Ob. 1 2
Cl. (B♭) 1 2
a 2
Fg. 1 2
a 2
Cor. (E♭) 1 2
a 2
Tr. (E♭) 1 2
Timp.
I
Vl.
II
Vla.
Vc.
Vc. e Cb.
222
Cl. (B♭) 1 2
Solo
Fg. 1 2
I
Vl.
II
Vla.
Vc.
Tutti
Vc.
Vc. e Cb.

228
1. Solo
Ob. 1 2
[p]
Cl. (B♭) 1 2
1.
Fg. 1 2
I
Vl.
II
Vla.
Vc.
Tutti
Vc. e Cb.
234
Fg. 1 2
1.
I
Vl.
II
Vla.
Vc. e Cb.

241
1. Solo
Ob. 1 2
p
Cl. (B♭) 1 2
p
1.
Fg. 1 2
I
Vl.
II
Vla.
Vc. e Cb.
247 [a 2]
Fl. 1 2
f
Tutti
Ob. 1 2
f
a 2
Cl. (B♭) 1 2
f
Tutti
Fg. 1 2
f
a 2
Cor. (E♭) 1 2
f
Tr. (E♭) 1 2
f
Timp.
f
I
Vl.
II
f
Vla.
f
Vc. e Cb.
f

253 [a 2]
Fl. 1 2
Ob. 1 2
a 2
Cl. (B♭) 1 2
a 2
Fg. 1 2
a 2
a 2
Cor. (E♭) 1 2
a 2
Tr. (E♭) 1 2
Timp.
I
Vl.
II
Vla.
Vc. e Cb.

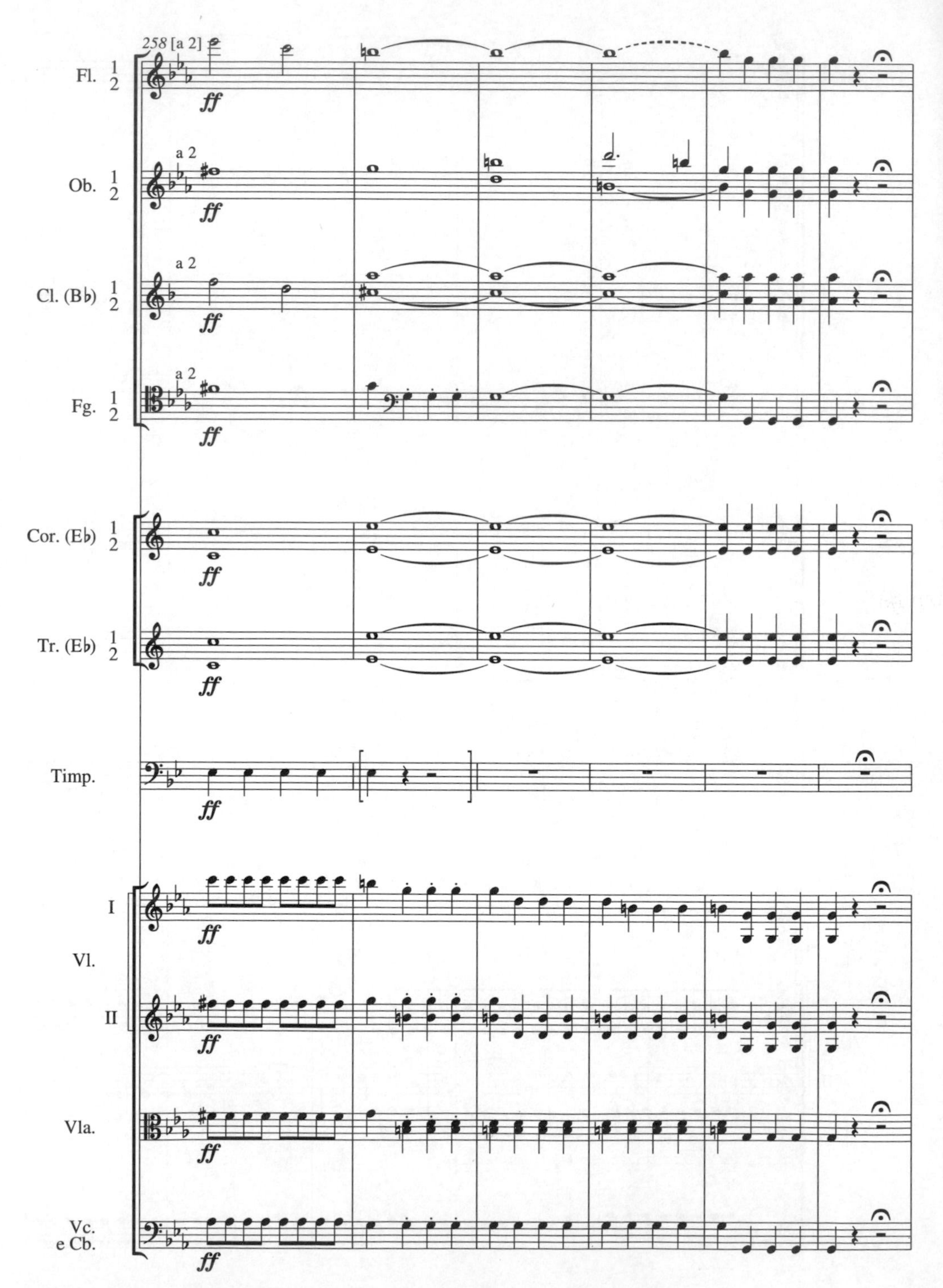
258 [a 2]
Fl. 1 2
ff
a 2
Ob. 1 2
ff
a 2
Cl. (B♭) 1 2
ff
a 2
Fg. 1 2
ff
Cor. (E♭) 1 2
ff
Tr. (E♭) 1 2
ff
Timp.
ff
I
Vl.
II
ff
ff
Vla.
ff
Vc. e Cb.
ff

264
Cl. (B♭) 1 2
Soli
Cor. (E♭) 1 2
I
Vl.
II
271
[a 2]
Fl. 1 2
a 2
Ob. 1 2
a 2
Cl. (B♭) 1 2
a 2
Fg. 1 2
Cor. (E♭) 1 2
a 2
Tr. (E♭) 1 2
Timp.
I
Vl.
II
Vla.
Vc. e Cb.

278 [a 2]
Fl. 1 2
Ob. 1 2
Cl. (B♭) 1 2
a 2
Fg. 1 2
a 2
Cor. (E♭) 1 2
a 2
Tr. (E♭) 1 2
a 2
Timp.
I
Vl.
II
Vla.
Vc. e Cb.

[a 2]
284
Fl. 1 2
Ob. 1 2
a 2
a 2
Cl. (B♭) 1 2
a 2
Fg. 1 2
a 2
Cor. (E♭) 1 2
a 2
Tr. (E♭) 1 2
Timp.
I
Vl.
II
Vla.
Vc.
e Cb.

290 [a 2]
Fl. 1 2
a 2
Ob. 1 2
a 2
Cl. (B♭) 1 2
a 2
Fg. 1 2
a 2
Cor. (E♭) 1 2
a 2
Tr. (E♭) 1 2
Timp.
I
Vl.
II
Vla.
Vc. e Cb.
fz

297
[a 2]
Fl. 1 2
fz
Ob. 1 2
fz
Cl. (B♭) 1 2
fz
a 2
Fg. 1 2
fz
a 2
a 2
Cor. (E♭) 1 2
a 2
Tr. (E♭) 1 2
Timp.
I
Vl.
II
fz
fz
Vla.
fz
Vc. e Cb.
fz

[a 2]
303
Fl. 1 2
Ob. 1 2
Cl. (B♭) 1 2
a 2
Fg. 1 2
Cor. (E♭) 1 2
Tr. (E♭) 1 2
Timp.
I
Vl.
II
Vla.
Vc. e Cb.

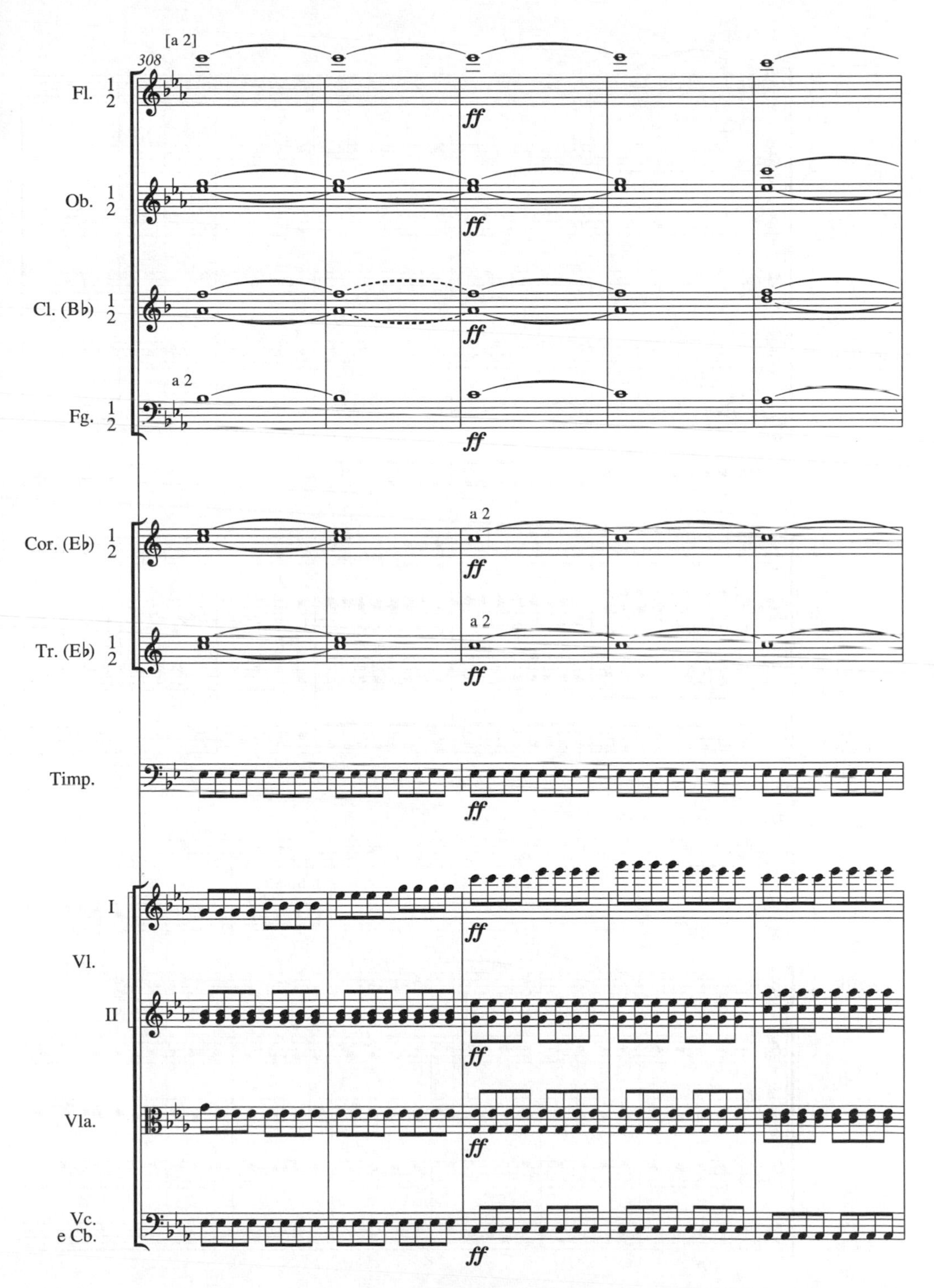
[a 2]
308
Fl. 1 2
Ob. 1 2
Cl. (B♭) 1 2
a 2
Fg. 1 2
Cor. (E♭) 1 2
a 2
Tr. (E♭) 1 2
a 2
Timp.
I
Vl.
II
Vla.
Vc. e Cb.
ff

[a 2]
313
Fl. 1 2
Ob. 1 2
Cl. (B♭) 1 2
a 2
Fg. 1 2
a 2
Cor. (E♭) 1 2
a 2
Tr. (E♭) 1 2
Timp.
I
Vl.
II
p
p
Vla.
p
Vc. e Cb.
319
Ob. 1 2
p
1. Solo
Cl. (B♭) 1 2
[p]
Cor. (E♭) 1 2
p
I
Vl.
II
Vla.
Vc. e Cb.
p

326
Solo
Fl. 1 2
p
Ob. 1 2
1.
Cl. (B♭) 1 2
Solo
Fg. 1 2
p
Cor. (E♭) 1 2
I
Vl.
II
Vla.
Vc. e Cb.
[1.]
333
Fl. 1 2
1.
Cl. (B♭) 1 2
1.
Fg. 1 2
Cor. (E♭) 1 2
I
Vl.
II
Vla.
Vc. e Cb.

339
[1.]
Fl. 1 2
[a 2]
f
Ob. 1 2
f
1.
Cl. (B♭) 1 2
Tutti
f
1.
Fg. 1 2
Tutti
f
Cor. (E♭) 1 2
f
Tr. (E♭) 1 2
f
Timp.
f
I
Vl.
II
f
f
Vla.
f
Vc. e Cb.
f

345
[a 2]
Fl. 1 2
Ob. 1 2
a 2
Cl. (B♭) 1 2
a 2
Fg. 1 2
Cor. (E♭) 1 2
Tr. (E♭) 1 2
Timp.
I
Vl.
II
Vla.
Vc. e Cb.
p
352
I
Vl.
II
Vla.
Vc. e Cb.

358
Fl. 1 2
[a 2]
f
Ob. 1 2
Cl. (B♭) 1 2
a 2
Fg. 1 2
a 2
Cor. (E♭) 1 2
a 2
Tr. (E♭) 1 2
Timp.
I
Vl.
II
Vla.
Vc. e Cb.

365
[a 2]
Fl. 1 2
Ob. 1 2
Cl. (B♭) 1 2
a 2
Fg. 1 2
Cor. (E♭) 1 2
Tr. (E♭) 1 2
Timp.
I
Vl.
II
Vla.
Vc. e Cb.

371
[a 2]
Fl. 1 2
Ob. 1 2
Cl. (B♭) 1 2
a 2
Fg. 1 2
Cor. (E♭) 1 2
Tr. (E♭) 1 2
Timp.
I
Vl.
II
Vla.
Vc. e Cb.

[a 2]
376
Fl. 1 2
Ob. 1 2
Cl. (B♭) 1 2
a 2
Fg. 1 2
Cor. (E♭) 1 2
Tr. (E♭) 1 2
Timp.
I
Vl.
II
Vla.
Vc. e Cb.

Fine Laus Deo

Printed in China